PABLO'S BIG DREAM

Written By Nathaniel Provencio
Illustrated By Jamie Sanford

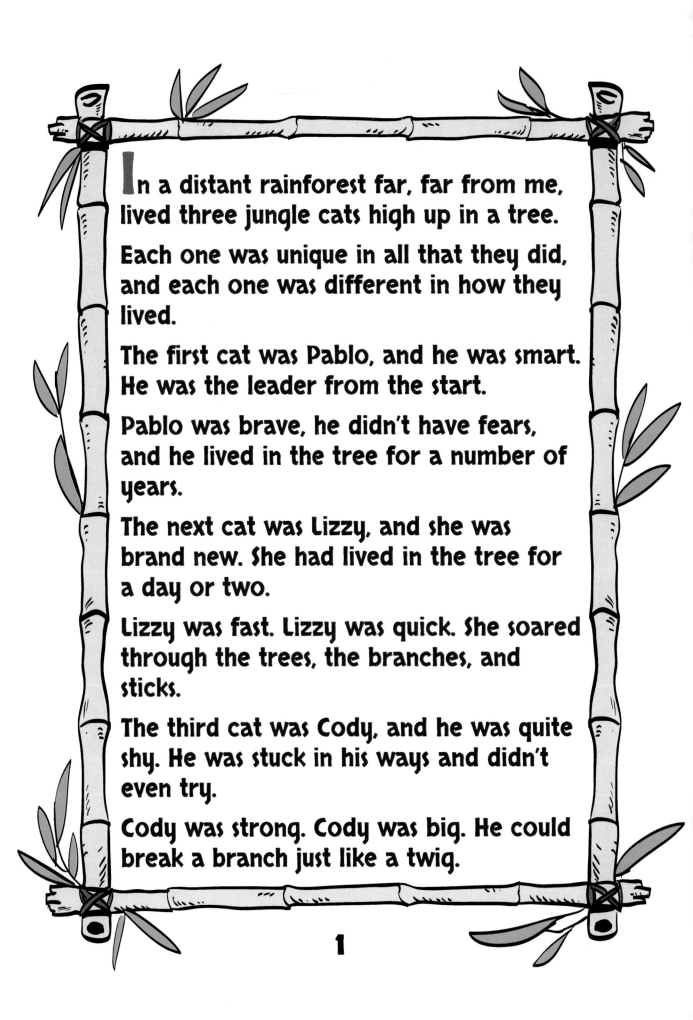

In a distant rainforest far, far from me, lived three jungle cats high up in a tree.

Each one was unique in all that they did, and each one was different in how they lived.

The first cat was Pablo, and he was smart. He was the leader from the start.

Pablo was brave, he didn't have fears, and he lived in the tree for a number of years.

The next cat was Lizzy, and she was brand new. She had lived in the tree for a day or two.

Lizzy was fast. Lizzy was quick. She soared through the trees, the branches, and sticks.

The third cat was Cody, and he was quite shy. He was stuck in his ways and didn't even try.

Cody was strong. Cody was big. He could break a branch just like a twig.

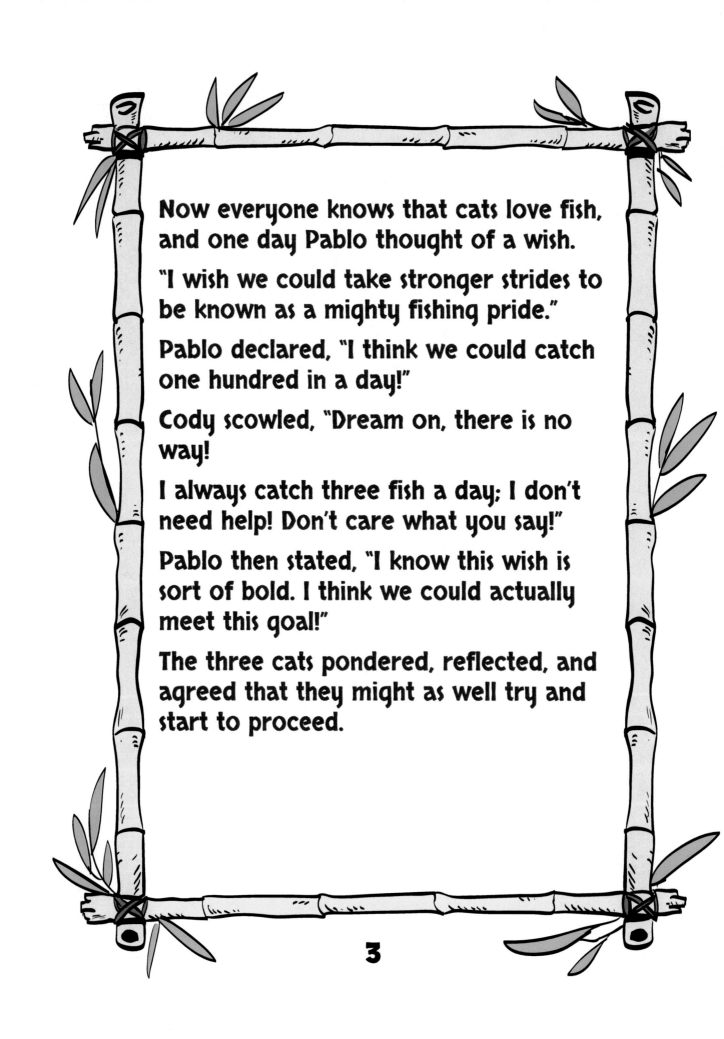

Now everyone knows that cats love fish, and one day Pablo thought of a wish.

"I wish we could take stronger strides to be known as a mighty fishing pride."

Pablo declared, "I think we could catch one hundred in a day!"

Cody scowled, "Dream on, there is no way!

I always catch three fish a day; I don't need help! Don't care what you say!"

Pablo then stated, "I know this wish is sort of bold. I think we could actually meet this goal!"

The three cats pondered, reflected, and agreed that they might as well try and start to proceed.

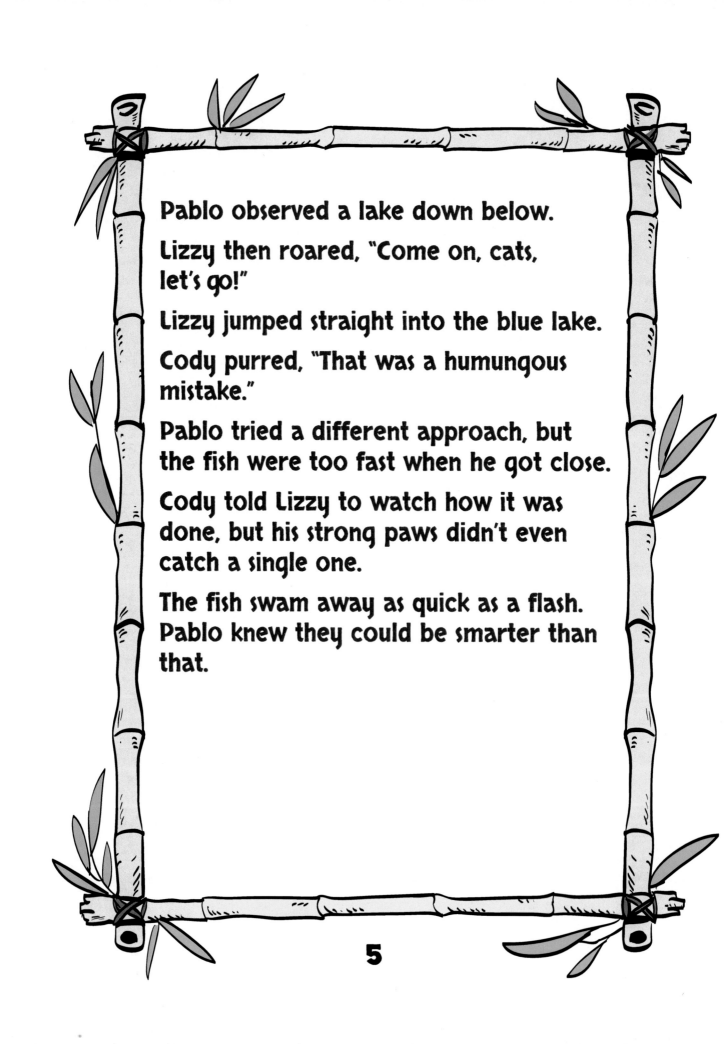

Pablo observed a lake down below.

Lizzy then roared, "Come on, cats, let's go!"

Lizzy jumped straight into the blue lake.

Cody purred, "That was a humungous mistake."

Pablo tried a different approach, but the fish were too fast when he got close.

Cody told Lizzy to watch how it was done, but his strong paws didn't even catch a single one.

The fish swam away as quick as a flash. Pablo knew they could be smarter than that.

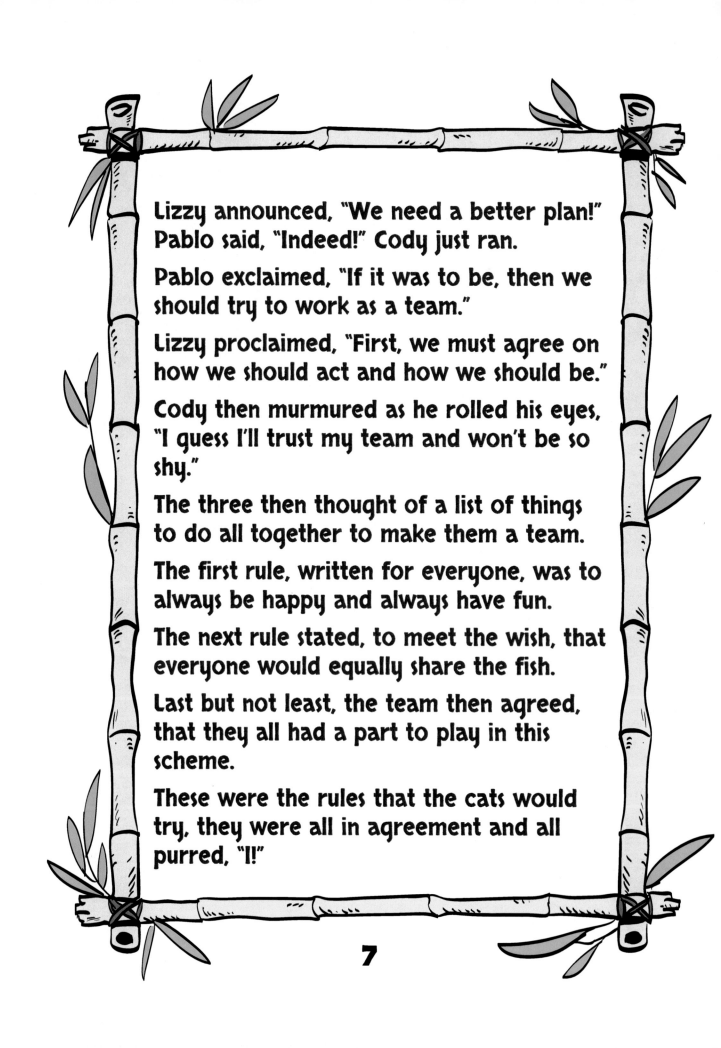

Lizzy announced, "We need a better plan!" Pablo said, "Indeed!" Cody just ran.

Pablo exclaimed, "If it was to be, then we should try to work as a team."

Lizzy proclaimed, "First, we must agree on how we should act and how we should be."

Cody then murmured as he rolled his eyes, "I guess I'll trust my team and won't be so shy."

The three then thought of a list of things to do all together to make them a team.

The first rule, written for everyone, was to always be happy and always have fun.

The next rule stated, to meet the wish, that everyone would equally share the fish.

Last but not least, the team then agreed, that they all had a part to play in this scheme.

These were the rules that the cats would try, they were all in agreement and all purred, "I!"

Now came the time to think of the plan where all cats would help and all lend a hand.

All three cats agreed on the goal, and all three cats agreed on their role.

Pablo would observe the fish from the tree; when the fish swam close, he would signal Lizzy.

Lizzy would run, pounce, dive, and leap, then snatch the fish with her very sharp teeth.

Cody would carry the fish to the tree and place them in a basket to keep.

The three all knew that they had skills and should work together so the basket would fill.

At first, the plan was going great. The cats were flawless and made no mistakes.

Lizzy, however, had other thoughts and started eating all the fish she had caught.

Pablo decided to raise his paw and call out this naughty behavior he saw.

"Lizzy, remember we need to be fair. All the fish will be equally shared."

Lizzy agreed she had made a mistake and promised to catch the fish that she ate.

Now the cats were back on track, collaborating with their strategic attack.

Pablo used a rock and some bark to keep track of the fish that the three cats had caught.

At first, the catch was sort of slow, but Pablo had faith they would meet their goal.

First, there were five fish, then twenty, then more. The fish piled in; the numbers did soar.

But after a while, their catch had declined; the cats were tired and were running out of time.

Pablo then cheered, "We are getting really close. Perhaps we need a different approach."

Cody perked up, "Let's take a quick break and move to a different part of the lake."

Lizzy agreed, and they adjusted a bit; the tasty fish were caught just as quick.

After some time, the cats met their mark! They celebrated each other and made some remarks.

Lizzy boasted with a smile and a grin that she was thankful for all of her friends.

Cody said he grew as a cat and a pal; he learned how to trust and was sorry he scowled.

Pablo's big plan had worked like a dream, but he needed his friends to work as a team.

Each cat ate thirty-three and a third, the fish were devoured, and then they all purred.

The three were now known all jungle wide as the forest's mightiest fishing pride.

Fat and full, the cats went to sleep and dreamed of the next goals they all would meet.

Eight Leadership Lessons for School Leaders

Pablo's Big Dream is a playful parable that demonstrates the power of leadership and collaboration. This book is not only written for children to enjoy but for classroom teachers and school leaders as well to help with conversations on leadership, school culture, and meeting the needs of all students. **Pablo's Big Dream** outlines many of the foundational elements of the power of collective teacher efficacy. In 2016, John Hattie, a professor of education and director of the Melbourne Education Research Institute at the University of Melbourne, authored the book, **Visible Learning**, which synthesized more than 800 meta-studies on educational techniques and their impact on student learning. Through this research, Hattie and his team discovered that collective Teacher Efficacy (CTE) was one of the most effective indicators related to positive student achievement.

Hattie, J., & Zierer, K. (2019). Visible Learning Insights. Routledge.

Collective Teacher Efficacy is defined as the collective belief of the school faculty in their ability to positively impact their students. A school staff that can collectively accomplish great things is vital for the health of a school, and if they believe they can make a positive difference, then they very likely will.

Admin, C. T. W. (2021, June 9). Collective teacher efficacy. CT3. Retrieved March 31, 2022, from:

https://www.ct3education.com/2021/06/09/collective-teacher-efficacy/

This powerful finding highlights the importance, relevance and significance a culture of collaboration can have for schools, teachers, families and students.

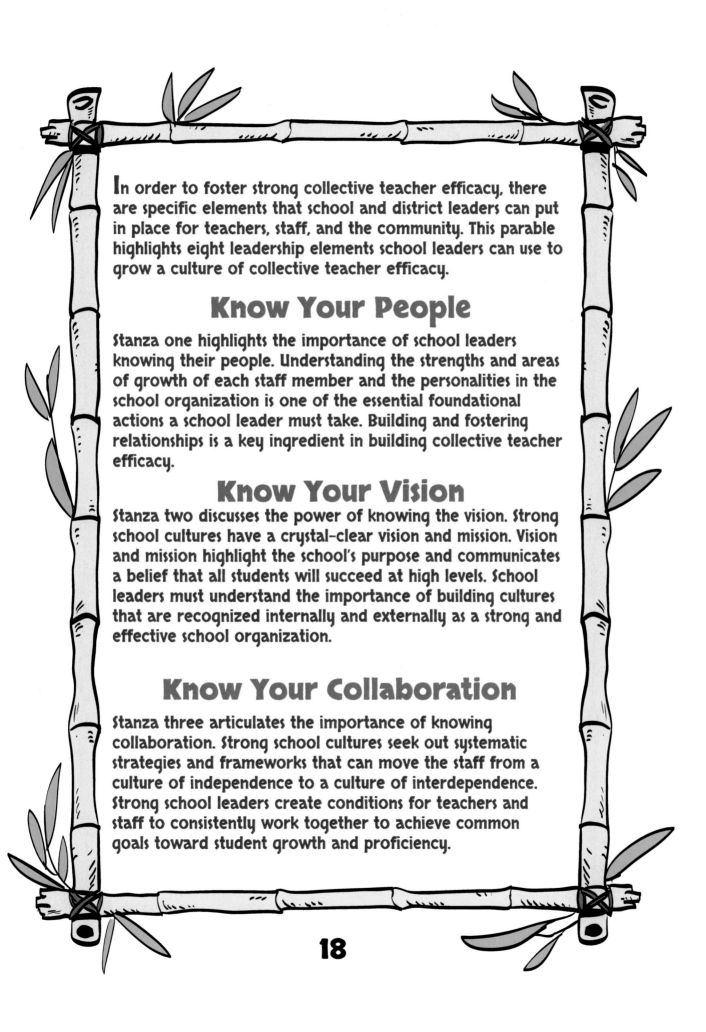

In order to foster strong collective teacher efficacy, there are specific elements that school and district leaders can put in place for teachers, staff, and the community. This parable highlights eight leadership elements school leaders can use to grow a culture of collective teacher efficacy.

Know Your People

Stanza one highlights the importance of school leaders knowing their people. Understanding the strengths and areas of growth of each staff member and the personalities in the school organization is one of the essential foundational actions a school leader must take. Building and fostering relationships is a key ingredient in building collective teacher efficacy.

Know Your Vision

Stanza two discusses the power of knowing the vision. Strong school cultures have a crystal-clear vision and mission. Vision and mission highlight the school's purpose and communicates a belief that all students will succeed at high levels. School leaders must understand the importance of building cultures that are recognized internally and externally as a strong and effective school organization.

Know Your Collaboration

Stanza three articulates the importance of knowing collaboration. Strong school cultures seek out systematic strategies and frameworks that can move the staff from a culture of independence to a culture of interdependence. Strong school leaders create conditions for teachers and staff to consistently work together to achieve common goals toward student growth and proficiency.

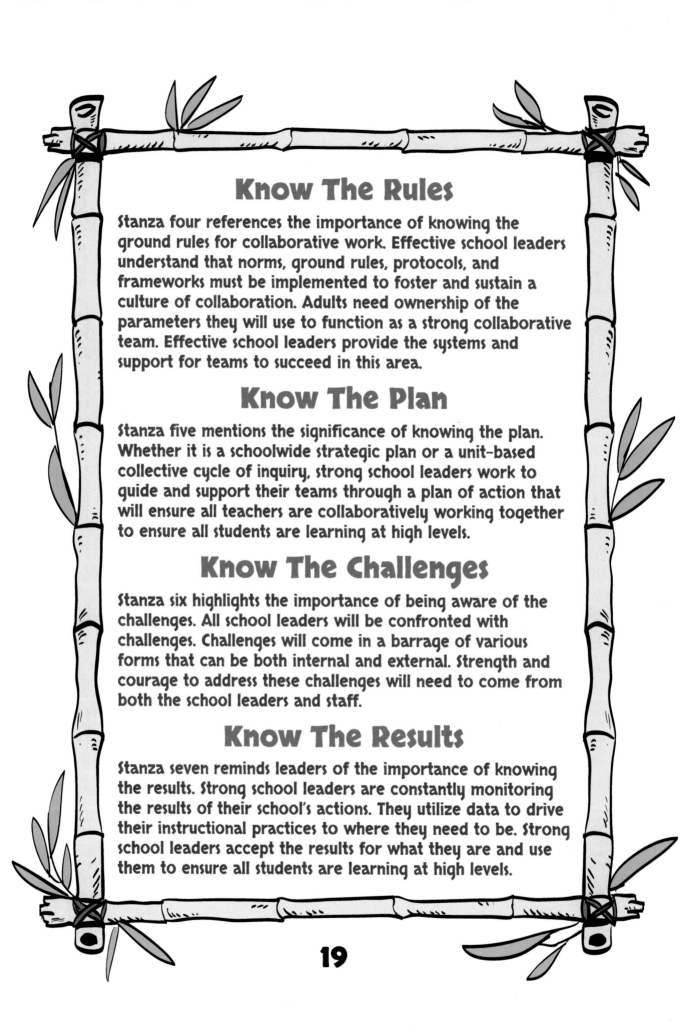

Know The Rules

Stanza four references the importance of knowing the ground rules for collaborative work. Effective school leaders understand that norms, ground rules, protocols, and frameworks must be implemented to foster and sustain a culture of collaboration. Adults need ownership of the parameters they will use to function as a strong collaborative team. Effective school leaders provide the systems and support for teams to succeed in this area.

Know The Plan

Stanza five mentions the significance of knowing the plan. Whether it is a schoolwide strategic plan or a unit-based collective cycle of inquiry, strong school leaders work to guide and support their teams through a plan of action that will ensure all teachers are collaboratively working together to ensure all students are learning at high levels.

Know The Challenges

Stanza six highlights the importance of being aware of the challenges. All school leaders will be confronted with challenges. Challenges will come in a barrage of various forms that can be both internal and external. Strength and courage to address these challenges will need to come from both the school leaders and staff.

Know The Results

Stanza seven reminds leaders of the importance of knowing the results. Strong school leaders are constantly monitoring the results of their school's actions. They utilize data to drive their instructional practices to where they need to be. Strong school leaders accept the results for what they are and use them to ensure all students are learning at high levels.

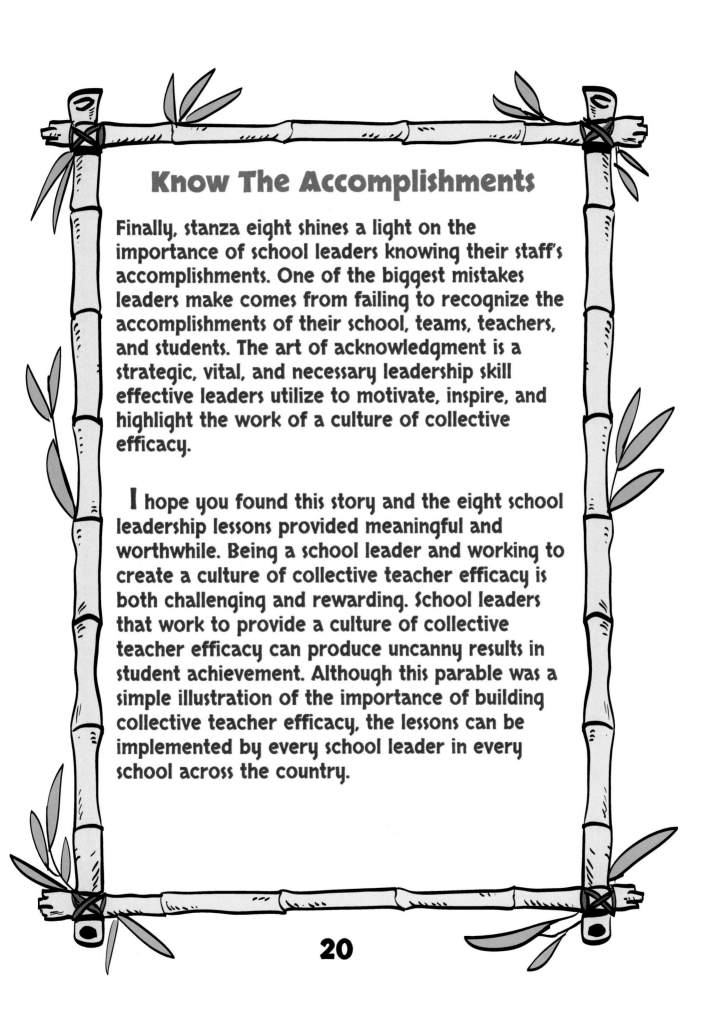

Know The Accomplishments

Finally, stanza eight shines a light on the importance of school leaders knowing their staff's accomplishments. One of the biggest mistakes leaders make comes from failing to recognize the accomplishments of their school, teams, teachers, and students. The art of acknowledgment is a strategic, vital, and necessary leadership skill effective leaders utilize to motivate, inspire, and highlight the work of a culture of collective efficacy.

I hope you found this story and the eight school leadership lessons provided meaningful and worthwhile. Being a school leader and working to create a culture of collective teacher efficacy is both challenging and rewarding. School leaders that work to provide a culture of collective teacher efficacy can produce uncanny results in student achievement. Although this parable was a simple illustration of the importance of building collective teacher efficacy, the lessons can be implemented by every school leader in every school across the country.

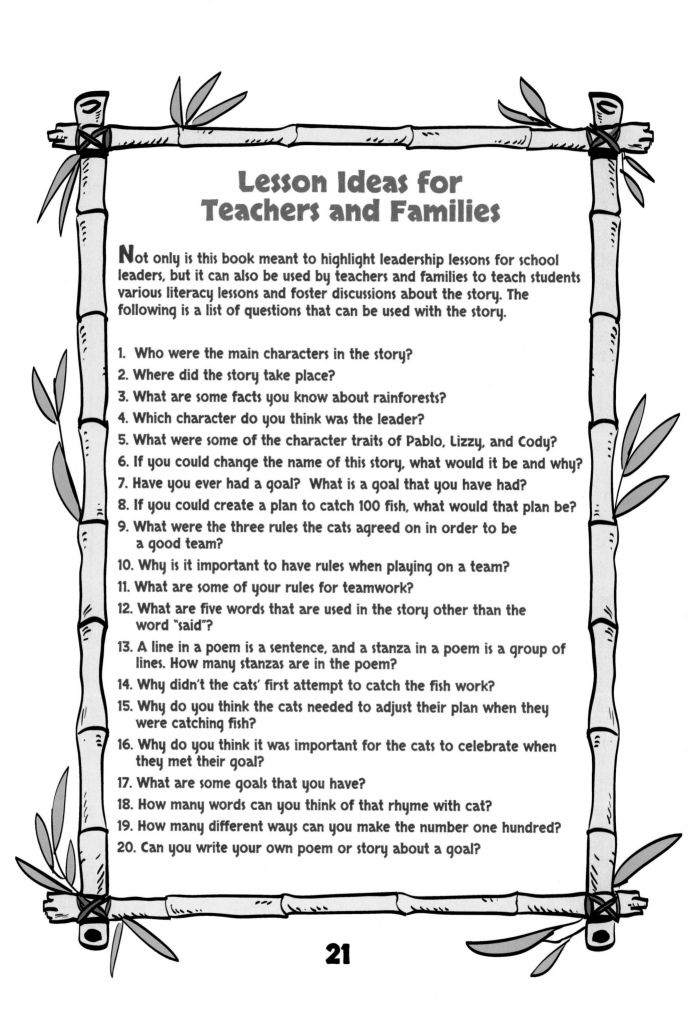

Lesson Ideas for Teachers and Families

Not only is this book meant to highlight leadership lessons for school leaders, but it can also be used by teachers and families to teach students various literacy lessons and foster discussions about the story. The following is a list of questions that can be used with the story.

1. Who were the main characters in the story?
2. Where did the story take place?
3. What are some facts you know about rainforests?
4. Which character do you think was the leader?
5. What were some of the character traits of Pablo, Lizzy, and Cody?
6. If you could change the name of this story, what would it be and why?
7. Have you ever had a goal? What is a goal that you have had?
8. If you could create a plan to catch 100 fish, what would that plan be?
9. What were the three rules the cats agreed on in order to be a good team?
10. Why is it important to have rules when playing on a team?
11. What are some of your rules for teamwork?
12. What are five words that are used in the story other than the word "said"?
13. A line in a poem is a sentence, and a stanza in a poem is a group of lines. How many stanzas are in the poem?
14. Why didn't the cats' first attempt to catch the fish work?
15. Why do you think the cats needed to adjust their plan when they were catching fish?
16. Why do you think it was important for the cats to celebrate when they met their goal?
17. What are some goals that you have?
18. How many words can you think of that rhyme with cat?
19. How many different ways can you make the number one hundred?
20. Can you write your own poem or story about a goal?

About the Author

Nathaniel Provencio is a career educator and author. He has served as a classroom teacher, school principal, and associate superintendent. Nathaniel is the CEO of ProvenPrincipal LLC, and he works with school leaders and teachers across the United States, supporting leadership development and school improvement strategies. He is the father of two amazing kids named Evan and Lily and has three cats named Val, Kiko, and Izzy, who were the inspiration for this story.

About the Illustrator

Jamie Sanford is a graduate of the Memphis College of Art with over twenty years of experience in the graphic design and illustration field. He has worked on numerous projects for all ages.

Made in the USA
Middletown, DE
02 October 2022

11675375R00015